Upti   5

preventive
maintenance

Uptime Elements™ are a trademark of Uptime® Magazine · ©2014 Uptime Magazine
uptimemagazine.com · reliabilityweb.com · maintenance.org

The Uptime Elements is a holistic system
Technical Elements • Cultural

uptime®
A Reliability System For

Rcm
reliability centered maintenance

Fmea
failure mode effects analysis

Ca
criticality analysis

Pmo
pm optimization

Rca
root cause analysis

Re
reliability engineering

Cp
capital project management

Aci
asset condition information

Vib
vibration analysis

Oa
oil analysis

Ut
ultrasound testing

Ir
infrared thermal imaging

Mt
motor testing

Ab
alignment and balancing

Ndt
non destructive testing

Lu
machinery lubrication

REM | Reliability Engineering for Maintenance

ACM | Asset Condition Management

Reliabilityweb.com's Asset Management Timeline

AM | Asset Management

Business Needs Analysis

Asset Plan

based approach to reliability that includes:
Elements • Leadership Elements

Elements™

Asset Performance Management

Preventive Maintenance

Pm — preventive maintenance

Ps — planning and scheduling

Odr — operator driven reliability

Mro — mro-spares management

De — defect elimination

Cmms — computerized maintenance management system

WEM — Work Execution Management

Opx — operational excellence

Kpi — key performance indicators

Pam — physical asset management

Hcm — human capital management

Int — integrity

Cbl — competency based learning

Es — executive sponsorship

LER — Leadership for Reliability

Design → Create → Operate / Maintain → Modify/Upgrade / Dispose

———————————— Asset Lifecycle ————————————→

Preventive Maintenance

©2014 Reliabilityweb.com
Printed in the United States of America.
All rights reserved.

Publisher: Terrence O'Hanlon

For information: Reliabilityweb.com
www.reliabilityweb.com
PO Box 60075, Ft. Myers, FL 33906
Toll Free: 888-575-1245 | Phone: 239-333-2500
E-mail: customerservice@reliabilityweb.com

10   9   8   7   6   5   4   3   2

Table Of Contents

1 Introduction

A *Preventive and Predictive Maintenance Technology* magazine study reveals that breakdown maintenance would cost a company approximately $17 to $18 per year per installed horsepower. However, if the company has an effective preventive maintenance program in place, the maintenance cost drops to $11 to $13 per installed horsepower per year. This clearly shows maintenance activities that are performed in a breakdown or reactive mode are much more expensive than maintenance that can be performed in a preventive or planned mode. Therefore, from a pure cost perspective, preventive maintenance has a distinct advantage.

2 Preventive Maintenance Goals

There are many goals for preventive maintenance (PM) programs. The first goal is to eliminate maintenance-related equipment downtime on equipment that is capacity constrained in order to gain additional capacity. By reducing the amount of maintenance-related downtime related to equipment failures, additional capacity is gained. This capacity can be utilized to either increase production rates for any products that it produces (where there is market demand) or eliminate any redundant equipment currently used to produce the product.

A secondary goal is to use the PM program to extend the usable life of the equipment, sometimes by as much as 40 percent. A third goal is to reduce the amount of reactive or breakdown work the maintenance organization performs. This increases maintenance productivity, thereby reducing maintenance costs.

An additional goal for a good PM program is to focus on reducing the equipment's energy consumption. For example, heat exchangers or coolers that are cleaned at the right frequency eliminates wasted energy. Also, improved coupling alignment accuracy eliminates wasted energy. Finally, there are regulatory agencies, process safety management and international standards organizations that all have requirements that are PM related. A good PM program will ensure the company focuses on these major goals.

3 Types of Preventive Maintenance Activities

Three basic activities form the foundation of a PM program. They are:

- Good equipment inspections and services,

- Proper lubrication,

- Proper fastening procedures.

Studies have shown that up to 50 percent of all equipment failures have a root cause in one of these three areas. If organizations focus on just these PM basics, most would see a reduction in the amount of reactive work they are performing and a subsequent increase in equipment availability and maintenance productivity.

4 Steps to Developing a Preventive Maintenance Program

There are basic steps for developing a good preventive maintenance program that adds value to an organization.

The first step is to investigate why the organization is developing or changing the PM program. In some cases, developing a PM program is necessary when new equipment is brought into a plant or facility. In many companies, however, a PM program already exists. In these cases, it is a matter of modifying the preventive maintenance program because of poor equipment performance, recommendations from maintenance reliability engineering based on equipment performance, or some environmental, health and safety requirements that have changed. Whatever the driver for change, it is good for senior management to endorse and support changes made to the PM program.

If the reason for developing the PM program is new equipment, then the person responsible for the development of the PM program should obtain all the pertinent information from the manufacturer. If the manufacturer's manual is not available or is very limited in scope, then the person can find a similar equipment item that currently exists in the plant. If this is not an option, then a similar equipment item may be found in another plant within the corporation. If this is not an available source of information, then existing equipment with a neighboring plant or even with a competitor's plant may be used as a baseline. Even if one of these methods were chosen, it would be good to consult with existing supervisors, technicians and maintenance engineers to ensure the PM program being developed is sufficient to accomplish its goals.

If the PM program is being modified for preexisting equipment, then all the current PM information should be collected for review. This would include all current PM tasks for the trades and technicians. It would also include gathering the equipment's history. This would allow for an investigation into the effectiveness of the preventive maintenance that currently exists. In addition, equipment histories should be consulted to find any equipment problems that have developed that are not currently addressed by the PM program. Once all this information is gathered, the PM requirements can be reviewed and any deficiencies noted. Armed with historical data and the existing PM program, the maintenance reliability engineer can then properly develop or modify the required PMs.

The next step is to determine PM requirements. Most companies use a calendar-based program, where typically there are daily, weekly, monthly, quarterly, semiannual, or annual tasks. Each of these PMs would then list a specific set of tasks or actions that must be taken for the PM. The more specific details provided for each task, the more successful the PM is going to be. For example, when a task says to check for leaks, specific fittings on the inlet side of the pump, specific fittings on the outlet side of the pump and certain valves, such as directional control valves or pressure relief valves, should be mentioned.

Often times, companies feel that experienced personnel or journeyman-level personnel should know how to check for things without specifying them. However, this is not always the case. In many companies, there are gaps in individuals' experience and/ or training. This will lead to poor results on inspections, which leads to negative feelings about the preventive maintenance program. In addition, many current training programs are not effective and lead to craft skills being insufficient without providing this level of detail.

Preventive maintenance tasks also allow for training of existing craft employees. A new technician can be assigned a PM and be shadowed by a supervisor or an experienced technician. As the supervisor observes the technician performing the PM step-by-step, coaching can be provided, if necessary. The supervisor can then certify that the employee can properly perform the PM task, allowing the technician to perform the task in the future without any supervision. This becomes a performance-based training program, also commonly called on-the-job training.

In addition to the detailed task description, the PM task should specify the bill of materials (BOM) for the PM. If the PM requires spare parts, such as filters, lubricants, etc., this should be specified to help eliminate any delays in performing the PM activity while the technician is gathering or hunting for spare parts. Specifying spare parts on the PM also prevents the scheduling of the PM without the parts being kitted or staged, which again, helps to increase labor productivity of the technician performing the PM.

Once the PM tasks have been detailed, the next step is linking them to the appropriate equipment. In most cases, this is done by a computerized maintenance management system (e.g., CMMS or EAM system), which allows a PM library to be developed so each library task is associated to one or more pieces of equipment.

The subsequent step is to set the maintenance planning and scheduling parameter. The scheduling parameter is a trigger to activate the preventive maintenance task. Some examples are calendar-based PMs, time-based PMs, usage-based PMs, or, in some advanced companies, condition-based PMs. Once the proper scheduling parameter is set, they are filed in the PM library until the schedule calls for them to be activated. A scheduling call is when the calendar time, the usage, or the measured condition has been exceeded. The computerized management system is notified and the system automatically generates the PM based on the scheduling call. It is then sent to the appropriate crew for execution.

When developing a PM program, there are several common mistakes to avoid. The first is trying to address the wrong types of failures with the PM program. It is difficult to develop a PM program to eliminate infant mortality failures, random failures, abuse or misuse of equipment, or normal wear out failures.

Basic PM programs should be used to address equipment failures that become obvious as the equipment begins the wear out phase of its life. These age-related wear outs or failures should be the focus of a basic PM program. As equipment becomes older, it requires closer attention to its maintenance. Major overhauls or major equipment rebuilds may partially reestablish the equipment's lifecycle curve. Good data analysis will allow an organization to be cost effective when determining the schedules for age-related preventive maintenance.

5 Key Performance Indicators for Preventive Maintenance

Four key performance indicators (KPIs) for preventive maintenance are recommended to begin with, realizing that others can be added/substituted as the PM program matures. They are:

- *Preventive maintenance schedule compliance* – Measured by comparing the PM tasks that are scheduled in a given time period (usually a week) to those that were actually completed in that given time period. This should be calculated as a percentage. While this number may be low when a PM program is first started, the indicator should be in the 95 percent or higher range for a more mature PM program.

- *Preventive maintenance planning accuracy* – Measured by comparing the estimated labor and material resources on the PM plan to those that were actually utilized while performing the

PM task. Calculated as a percentage, this number should be in the 95 percent or higher range to enable good scheduling of PM tasks.

- *Preventive maintenance tasks overdue* – Looks at the PMs that were scheduled but not completed within a given time frame. The difficulty in using this indicator is setting a policy of when a PM is overdue. Is a weekly PM overdue a day after it was specified to be performed? A week? A month? Once the policy is properly set for each type of PM, the indicator can be extremely useful in keeping the PM program on schedule.

- *Preventive maintenance results* – Measured in several ways, however, the most common is to compare the reactive or breakdown maintenance work as a percentage of the total maintenance work performed. If a PM program is effective, the total amount of reactive maintenance work should be less than 20 percent of the total work performed. Reactive work should be clearly defined and tracked. For example, a common definition of reactive work is any work that is not scheduled a week in advance; in some organizations this is also known as scheduled break work, since it has to break into the weekly schedule to be performed.

6 What Every Reliability Leader Should Know about Preventive Maintenance

- Preventive maintenance forms the foundation of any maintenance and reliability process.

- The entire organization needs to value the PM process.

- The PM checksheets need to be detailed so they can be used to train new technicians.

- The PM program should focus on eliminating "wear out" equipment failures.

- PM programs should reduce the amount of reactive work to less than 20 percent of the maintenance activities.

7 Summary

Preventive maintenance is one of the most important building blocks of work execution management. It provides the stability necessary for the maintenance organization to become efficient and effective in other work execution management requirements. Without an effective PM program, organizations will continue to be stuck in a reactive mode of work.

8 References

Wireman, Terry. *Zero Breakdown Strategies*. Fort Myers: Reliabilityweb.com, 2012.

Wireman, Terry. *Maintenance Strategy Series Volume 1 - Preventive Maintenance*. Fort Myers: Reliabilityweb.com, 2011.

CRL Body of Knowledge

Reliability Leadership Travel Guide

Uptime Elements Passport Series

The (New) Asset Management Handbook: A Guide to ISO55000

Don't Just Fix It – Improve It by Winston P. Ledet, Winston J. Ledet and Sherri Abshire

Level 5 Leadership at Work by Winston P. Ledet, Michelle Ledet Henley and Sherri Abshire

People – A Reliability Success Story by Cliff Williams

Clean, Green and Reliable – A Sustainable Reliability Guide for Industrial Plants by Douglas Plucknette and Chris Colson

All books are available at
www.mro-zone.com

Acknowledgement

Development of the concepts expressed in the Certified Reliability Leader (CRL) body of knowledge (BoK) concept could not have happened without contributions from true masters in the reliability and asset management communities such as Paul Barringer, Dr. Robert Abernathy, Jack Nicolas Jr., Anthony "Mac" Smith, Ron Moore, Brad Peterson, Terry Wireman, Terry O'Hanlon, David McKeown, Bob DiStefano, Jason Tranter, Steve Turner, Jeff Shiver, Jeff Smith, Joel Levitt, Ramesh Gulati, Winston Ledet, June Ledet, Michelle Ledet Henley, Steve Thomas, Cliff Williams, Heinz Bloch, Christer Idhammer, Ralph Buscarello, Edmea Adell, Celso de Azevedo, John Hardwick, John Woodhouse, Jeff Smith, Grahame Fogel, John Schultz (and the Allied Reliability Group team), PJ Vlock, George Williams, George Mahoney, the entire AEDC/Jacobs/ATA team led by Bart Jones along with many more people who have been kind and generous in ensuring that original ideas and best practices are published and shared.

Further critical and editorial refinement was made by the Reliabilityweb.com/ Uptime Magazine team of Terrence O'Hanlon, Kelly Rigg O'Hanlon, Jenny Brunson, Bill Partipilo, Becky Partipilo, Kaitie Sweet, and Thayne Farrier.

Associations such as AMP, SMRP, GFMAM, Abraman, NAMS, IPWEA, AFE, ICML, STLE, ASME, and IAM have also created a foundation for this work through their efforts to create guidance, metrics and an ever-expanding body of knowledge around maintenance, reliability and asset management practices.

Complete Your Journey

Expand your knowledge.

Take the journey through all elements in a particular domain or complete the journey with the entire Uptime Elements chart.

Costs:

Individual Elements .... $5.99 each

Complete Domain .... $4.99 each

Complete Uptime Elements
Library (29) .... $3.99 each

If interested in large quantities for company-wide training, please contact us for a quote.

How to Order

To order, please visit:
www.mro-zone.com
888-575-1245 or 239-333-2500

Notes

Notes